great songs

arranged for ukulele

Wise Publications
part of The Music Sales Group
London/New York/Paris/Sydney/Copenhagen/Berlin/Madrid/Tokyo

Published by:
Wise Publications,
14-15 Berners Street, London W1T 3LJ, UK.

Exclusive Distributors:
Music Sales Limited,
Distribution Centre, Newmarket Road, Bury St Edmunds,
Suffolk IP33 3YB, UK.
Music Sales Pty Limited,
20 Resolution Drive, Caringbah, NSW 2229, Australia.

Order No. AM996930
ISBN 978-1-84938-008-9
This book © Copyright 2009 Wise Publications,
a division of Music Sales Limited.

Music arranged and engraved by shedwork.com
Cover designed by Fresh Lemon.
Photographs courtesy of Matthew Ward.

Printed in the EU .

Your Guarantee of Quality
As publishers, we strive to produce every book to the highest
commercial standards.

The music has been freshly engraved and the book has been carefully designed
to minimise awkward page turns and to make playing from it a real pleasure.

Particular care has been given to specifying acid-free, neutral-sized
paper made from pulps which have not been elemental chlorine bleached.

This pulp is from farmed sustainable forests and was produced with
special regard for the environment.

Throughout, the printing and binding have been planned to ensure
a sturdy, attractive publication which should give years of enjoyment.

If your copy fails to meet our high standards, please inform us
and we will gladly replace it.

www.musicsales.com

all i have to do is dream

Words & Music by Boudleaux Bryant

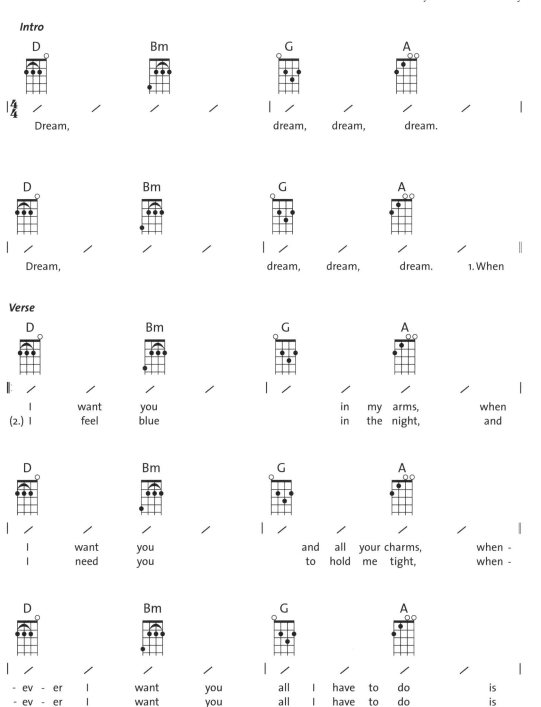

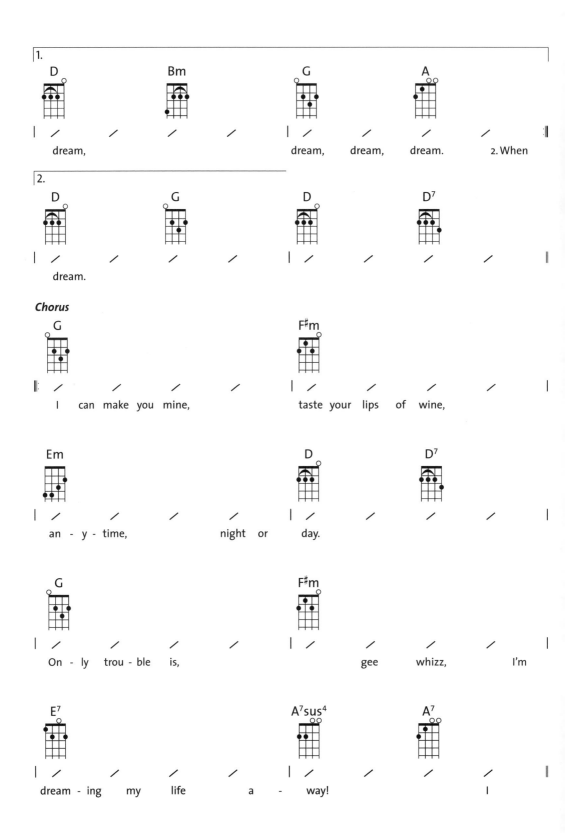

1.

| D | Bm | G | A |

/ / / / | / / / / ‖

dream, dream, dream, dream. 2. When

2.

| D | G | D | D⁷ |

/ / / / | / / / / ‖

dream.

Chorus

| G | F♯m |

‖: / / / / | / / / / |

I can make you mine, taste your lips of wine,

| Em | D | D⁷ |

| / / / / | / / / / |

an - y - time, night or day.

| G | F♯m |

| / / / / | / / / / |

On - ly trou - ble is, gee whizz, I'm

| E⁷ | A⁷sus⁴ | A⁷ |

| / / / / | / / / / ‖

dream - ing my life a - way! |

4

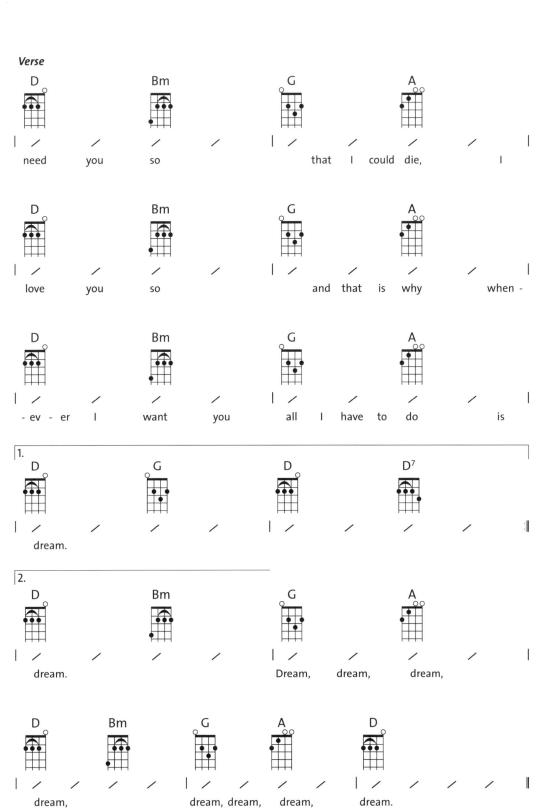

Verse

D   Bm   G   A

need   you   so   that   I   could   die,   I

D   Bm   G   A

love   you   so   and   that   is   why   when -

D   Bm   G   A

- ev - er   I   want   you   all   I   have   to   do   is

1.

D   G   D   D^7

dream.

2.

D   Bm   G   A

dream.   Dream,   dream,   dream,

D   Bm   G   A   D

dream,   dream, dream,   dream,   dream.

bring me sunshine

Words by Sylvia De
Music by Arthur Ken

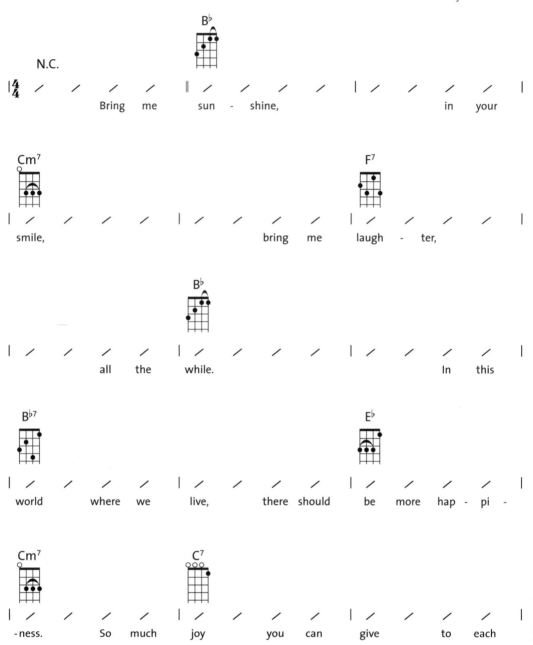

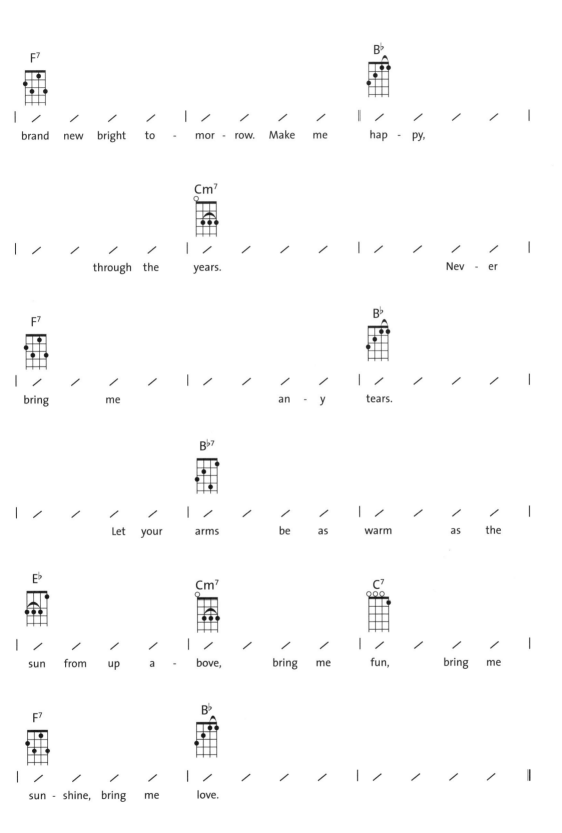

F⁷ · · · · | B♭ · · · · ‖ · · · ·
brand new bright to - mor - row. Make me hap - py,

Cm⁷ · · · · | · · · · | · · · ·
through the years. Nev - er

F⁷ · · · · | · · · · | B♭ · · · ·
bring me an - y tears.

B♭⁷ · · · · | · · · · | · · · ·
Let your arms be as warm as the

E♭ · · · · | Cm⁷ · · · · | C⁷ · · · ·
sun from up a - bove, bring me fun, bring me

F⁷ · · · · | B♭ · · · · | · · · ·
sun - shine, bring me love.

crazy

Words & Music by Willie Nelson

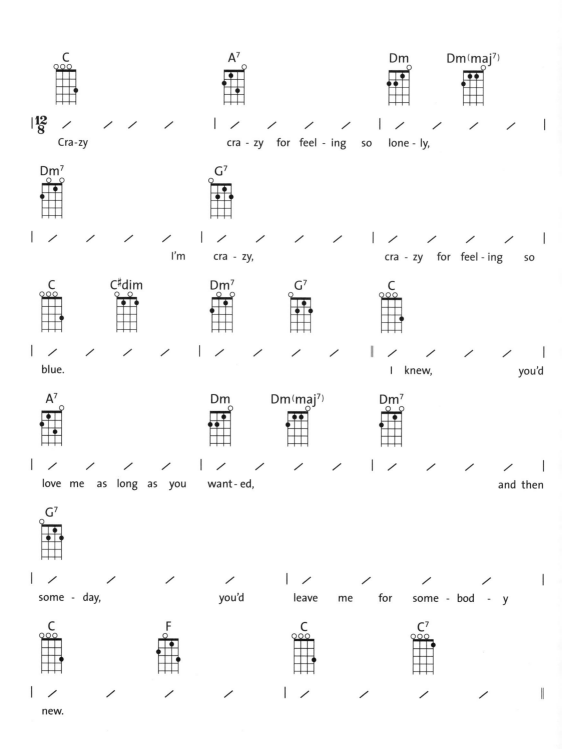

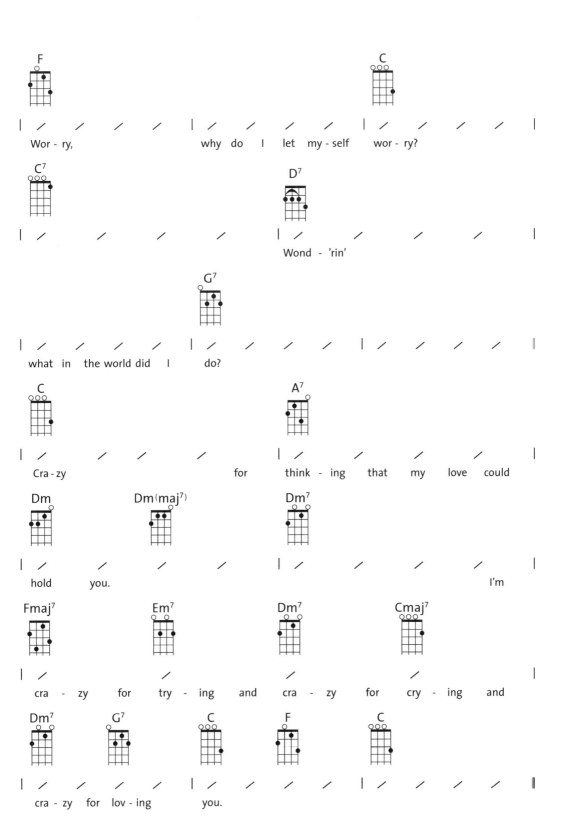

Wor - ry, why do I let my - self wor - ry?

Wond - 'rin'

what in the world did I do?

Cra - zy for think - ing that my love could

hold you. I'm

cra - zy for try - ing and cra - zy for cry - ing and

cra - zy for lov - ing you.

every breath you take

Words & Music by Sting

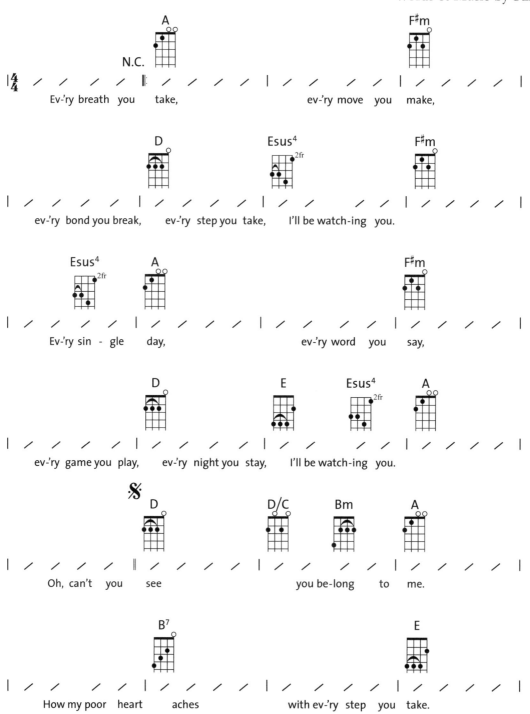

Ev-'ry breath you take, ev-'ry move you make,

ev-'ry bond you break, ev-'ry step you take, I'll be watch-ing you.

Ev-'ry sin - gle day, ev-'ry word you say,

ev-'ry game you play, ev-'ry night you stay, I'll be watch-ing you.

Oh, can't you see you be-long to me.

How my poor heart aches with ev-'ry step you take.

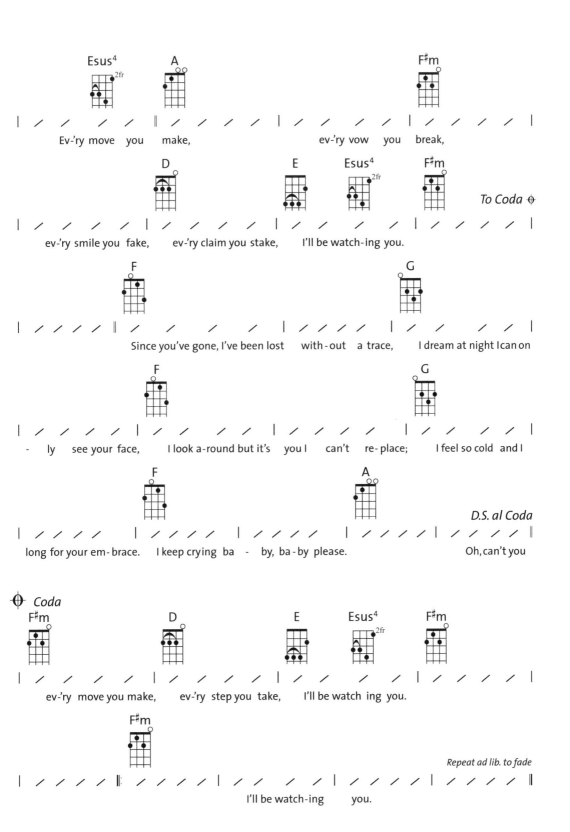

golden touch

Words & Music by Johnny Borrel

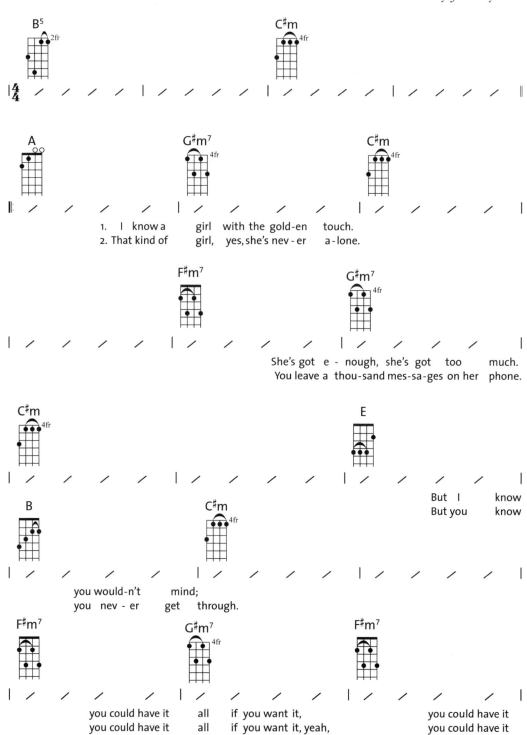

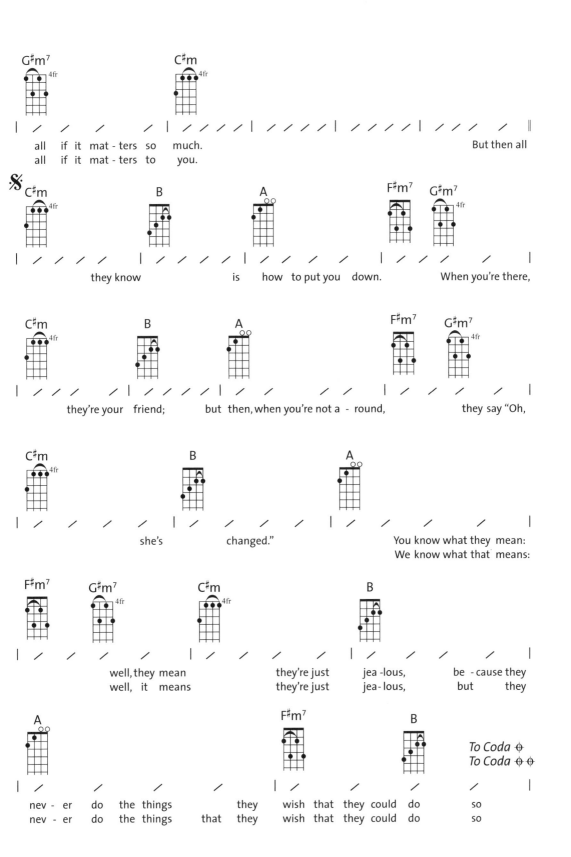

all if it mat - ters so much. But then all
all if it mat - ters to you.

they know is how to put you down. When you're there,

they're your friend; but then, when you're not a - round, they say "Oh,

she's changed." You know what they mean:
We know what that means:

well, they mean they're just jea - lous, be - cause they
well, it means they're just jea - lous, but they

nev - er do the things they wish that they could do so
nev - er do the things that they wish that they could do so

To Coda ⊕
To Coda ⊕⊕

13

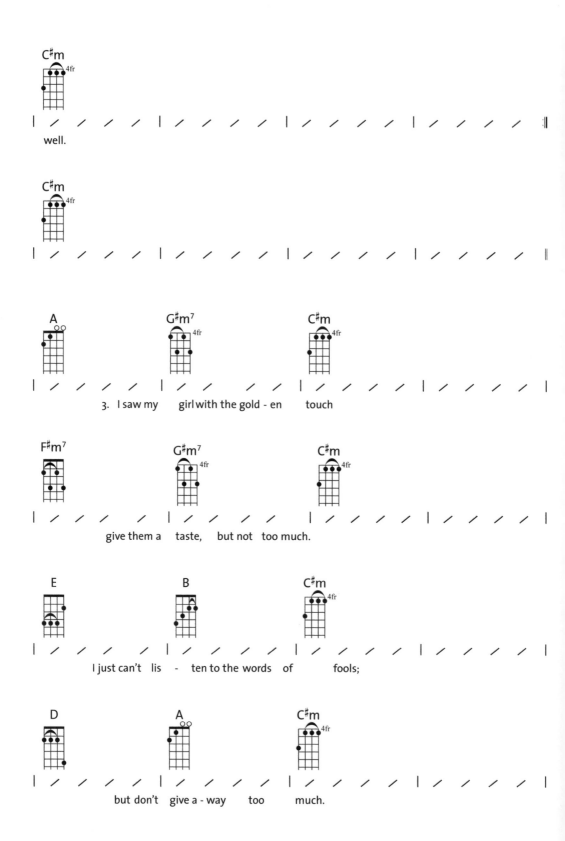

well.

3. I saw my girl with the gold - en touch

give them a taste, but not too much.

I just can't lis - ten to the words of fools;

but don't give a - way too much.

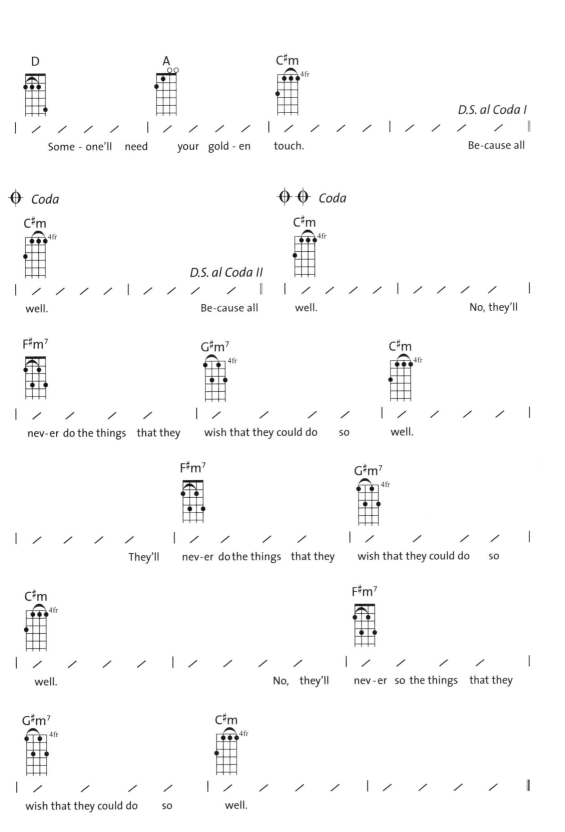

D   A   C♯m

D.S. al Coda I

Some - one'll need   your gold - en   touch.   Be-cause all

Coda   *Coda*

C♯m   C♯m

D.S. al Coda II

well.   Be-cause all   well.   No, they'll

F♯m⁷   G♯m⁷   C♯m

nev-er do the things that they   wish that they could do   so   well.

F♯m⁷   G♯m⁷

They'll   nev-er do the things that they   wish that they could do   so

C♯m   F♯m⁷

well.   No, they'll   nev-er so the things that they

G♯m⁷   C♯m

wish that they could do   so   well.

15

hallelujah

Words & Music by Leonard Cohen

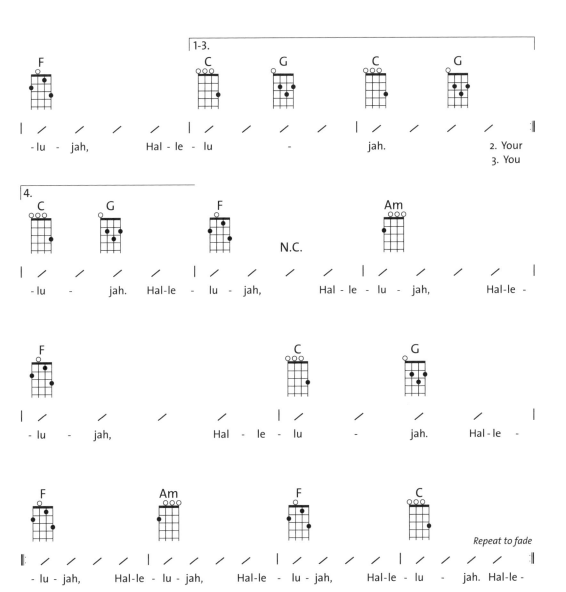

2. Your
3. You

F   -lu - jah,   **C**   Hal - le - lu   **G**   -   **C**   jah.   **G**

4.
C   -lu -   **G**   jah.   Hal-le   **F**   - lu - jah,   N.C.   Hal - le - lu - jah,   **Am**   Hal-le -

F   - lu - jah,   Hal - le - lu   **C**   -   **G**   jah.   Hal - le -

F   - lu - jah,   **Am**   Hal-le - lu - jah,   **F**   Hal-le - lu - jah,   **C**   Hal-le - lu - jah. Hal-le -

Repeat to fade

Verse 3
You say I took the name in vain
I don't even know the name
But if I did, well really, what's it to you?
There's a blaze of light in every word
It doesn't matter which you heard
The holy or the broken Hallelujah.

Hallelujah *etc.*

Verse 4
I did my best, it wasn't much
I couldn't feel, so I tried to touch
I've told the truth, I didn't come to fool you.
And even though it all went wrong
I'll stand before the Lord of Song
With nothing on my tongue but Hallelujah.

Hallelujah *etc.*

highway to hell

Words & Music by Angus Young, Malcolm Young & Bon Scott

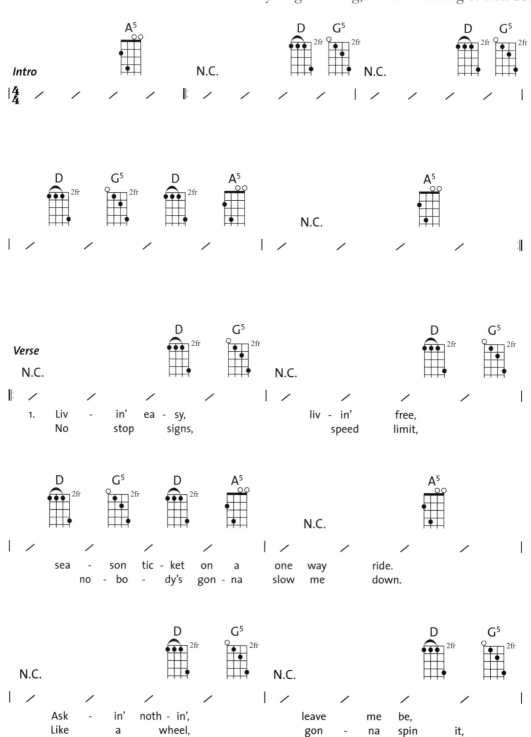

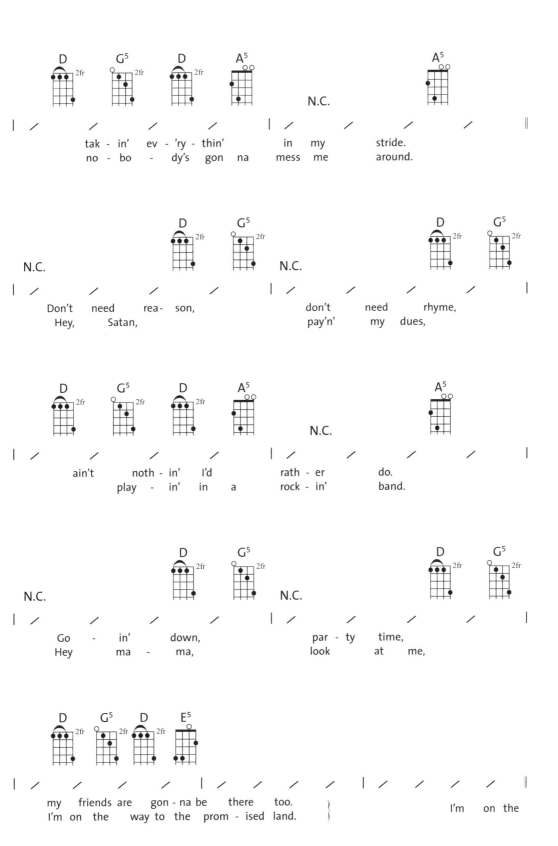

tak - in' ev - 'ry - thin'   in my   stride.
no - bo - dy's gon na   mess me   around.

Don't   need   rea- son,   don't   need   rhyme,
Hey,   Satan,   pay'n'   my   dues,

ain't   noth - in' I'd   rath - er   do.
play - in' in a   rock - in'   band.

Go -   in'   down,   par - ty   time,
Hey   ma -   ma,   look   at   me,

my   friends are   gon - na be   there   too.
I'm on the   way to the   prom - ised land.   I'm   on the

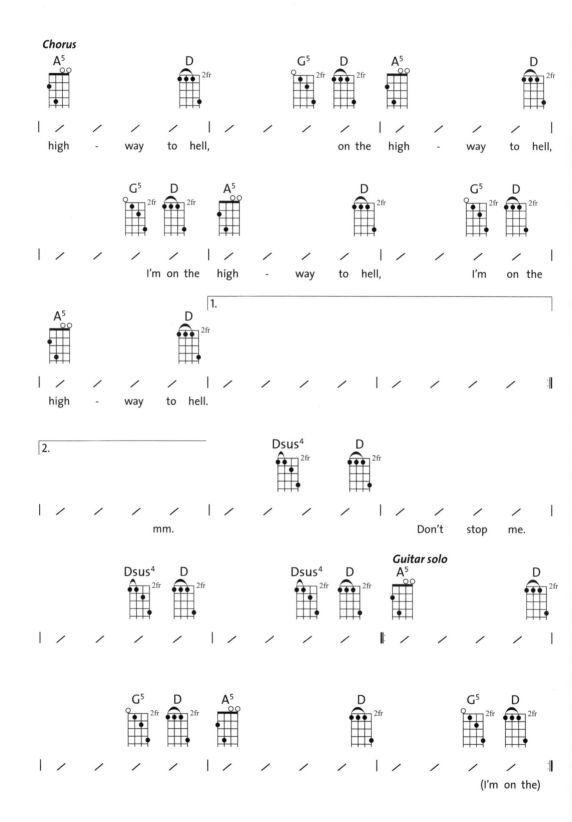

Chorus

high - way to hell,   on the high - way to hell,

I'm on the high - way to hell,   I'm on the

1.

high - way to hell.

2.   mm.   Don't stop me.

Guitar solo

(I'm on the)

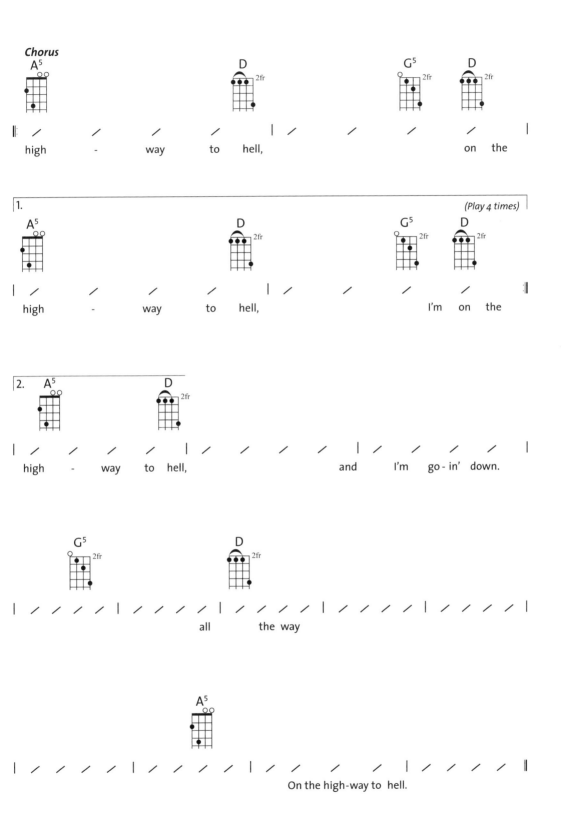

how deep is your love

Words & Music by Barry Gibb, Maurice Gibb & Robin Gibb

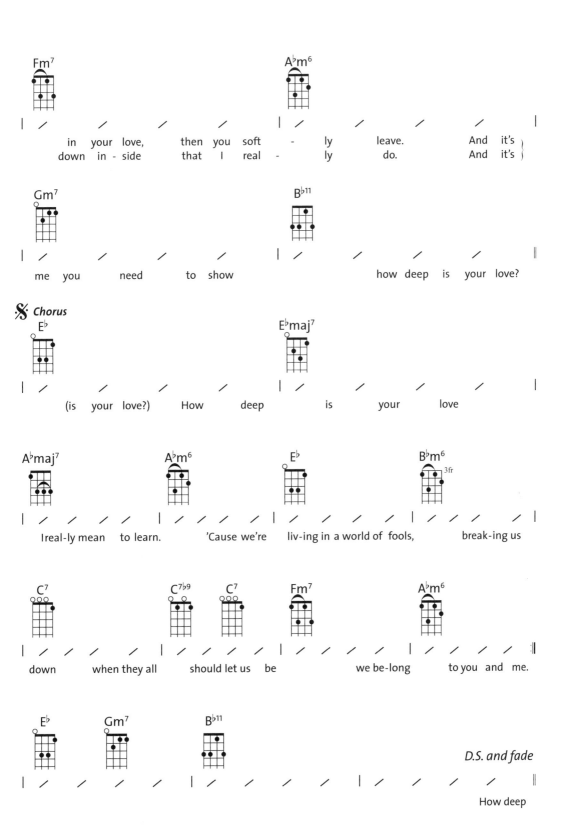

Fm⁷   A♭m⁶

in   your   love,   then   you   soft   -   ly   leave.   And   it's
down   in - side   that   I   real   -   ly   do.   And   it's

Gm⁷   B♭11

me   you   need   to   show   how   deep   is   your   love?

Chorus

E♭   E♭maj⁷

(is   your   love?)   How   deep   is   your   love

A♭maj⁷   A♭m⁶   E♭   B♭m⁶ 3fr

I real-ly mean   to learn.   'Cause we're   liv-ing in a world of fools,   break-ing us

C⁷   C⁷♭9   C⁷   Fm⁷   A♭m⁶

down   when they all   should let us   be   we be-long   to you   and   me.

E♭   Gm⁷   B♭11

D.S. and fade

How deep

23

i predict a riot

Words & Music by Nicholas Hodgson, Richard Wilson,
Andrew White, James Rix & Nicholas Baines

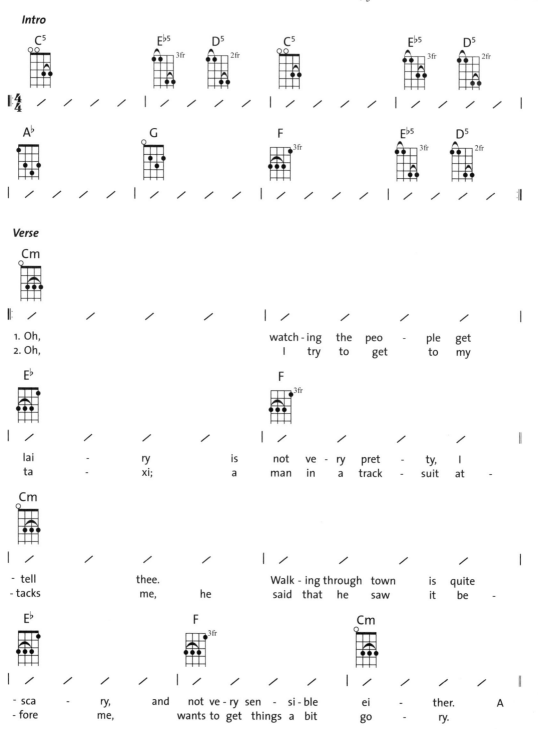

%

Cm

friend of a friend, he got
Girls run a - round with no
(3.) watch - ing the peo - ple get

E♭

beat - en, he
clothes on to
lai - ry is

F 3fr

looked the wrong way at a po - lice
bor - row a pound for a con
not ve - ry pret - ty I tell

Cm

- man; would
- dom; if it
thee.

E♭

ne - ver have hap - pened to Smea - ton, an
was - n't for chip - fat they'd be fro - zen. They're
Walk - ing through town is quite sca - ry, and

F 3fr

old Le - o - den - si - an.
not ve - ry sen - si - ble.
not ve - ry sen - si - ble.

Cm

La - a - a - a

G/B

B♭

la, la, la, la, la, la.

F 3fr

G/B

Ah - a - a -

Cm

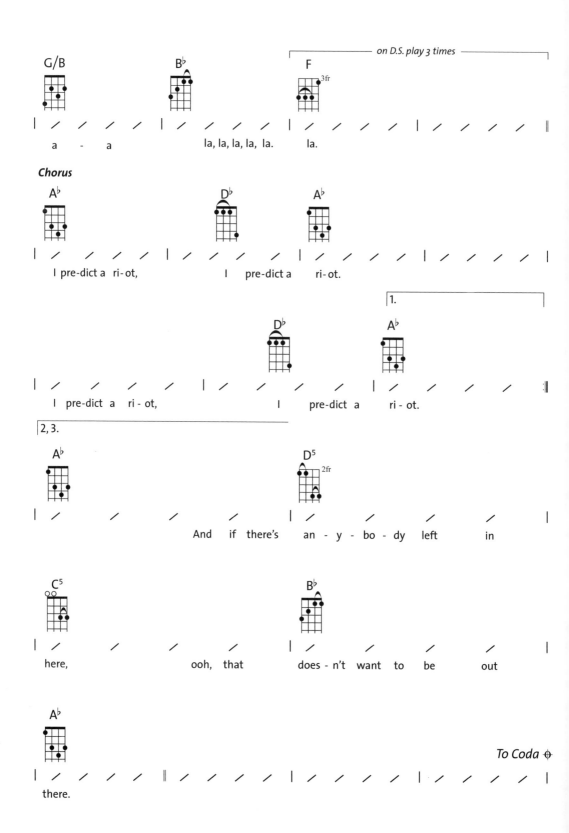

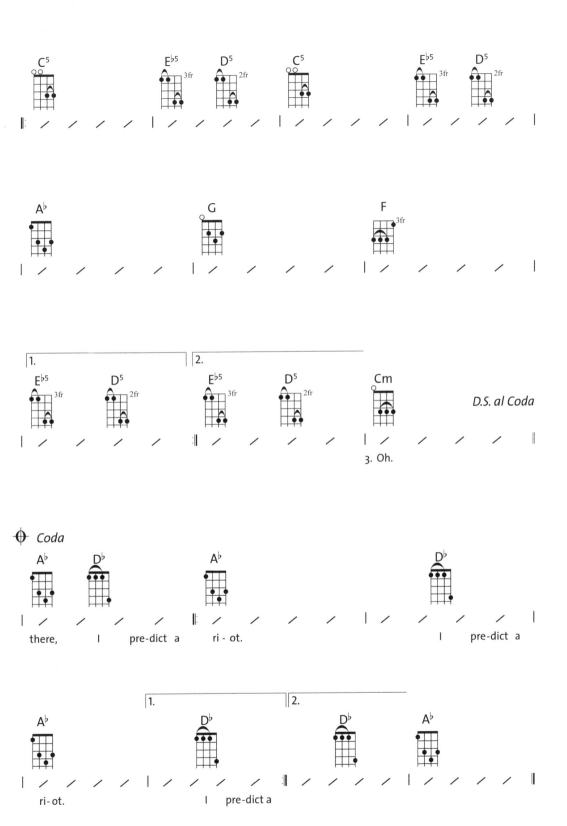

i shot the sheriff

Words & Music by Bob Marley

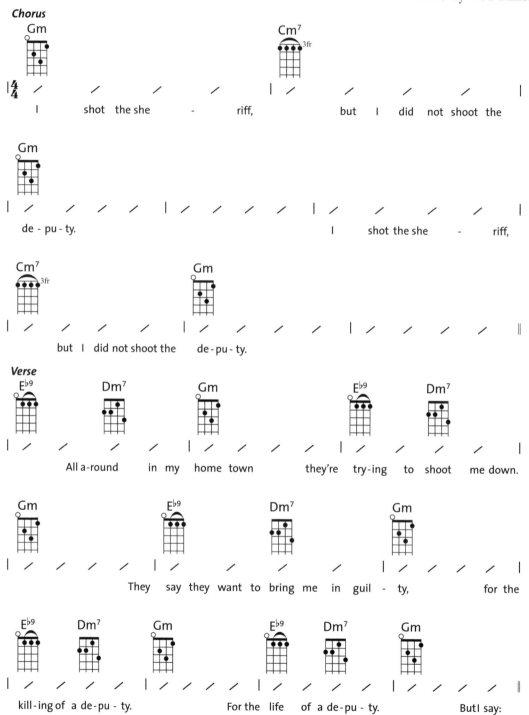

Riff

Chorus 2
I shot the sheriff
But I swear it was in self-defence.
I shot the sheriff
And they say it is a capital offence.

Verse 2
Sheriff John Brown always hated me
For what I don't know
And every time that I plant a seed
He said "Kill it, before it grows"
He said "Kill it, before it grows".

Chorus 3
I shot the sheriff
But I swear it was in self-defence
I shot the sheriff
And they say it is a capital offence.

Verse 3
Freedom came my way one day
And I started out of town there.
All of a sudden I see Sheriff John Brown
Aiming to shot me down
So I shot, I shot him down,
And I say

Chorus 4 & 5
I shot the sheriff
But I did not shoot the deputy.
I shot the sheriff
But I did not shoot the deputy.

Verse 4
Reflexes got the better of me
And what must be must be.
Every day the bucket goes to the well
But one day the bottom will drop out,
Yes, one day the bottom will drop out.

i will survive

Words & Music by Dino Fekaris & Freddie Perren

N.C.

Am Dm
1. At first I was a-fraid, I was pet-ri-fied, kept think-in'
(2.) go! Walk out the door. Just turn a-round
(3.) all the strength I had not to fall a-part, kept try-in'

G Cmaj7
I could ne-ver live with-out you by my side; but then I
now 'cause you're not wel-come an-y-more.
hard to mend the piec-es of my bro-ken heart; and I spent

Fmaj7 Bm7b5
spent so ma-ny nights think-in' how you did me wrong and I grew
Weren't you the one who tried to hurt me with good-bye? Did you think I'd crum-
oh so ma-ny nights just feel-in' sor-ry for my-self; I used to cry

E7sus4 E7
strong and I learned how to get a-long. And so you're
-ble Did you think I'd lay down and die? Oh no, not
but now I hold my head up high. And you see

Am Dm
back from out-er space I just walked
I, I will sur-vive. Oh, as
me some-bo-dy new. I'm not that

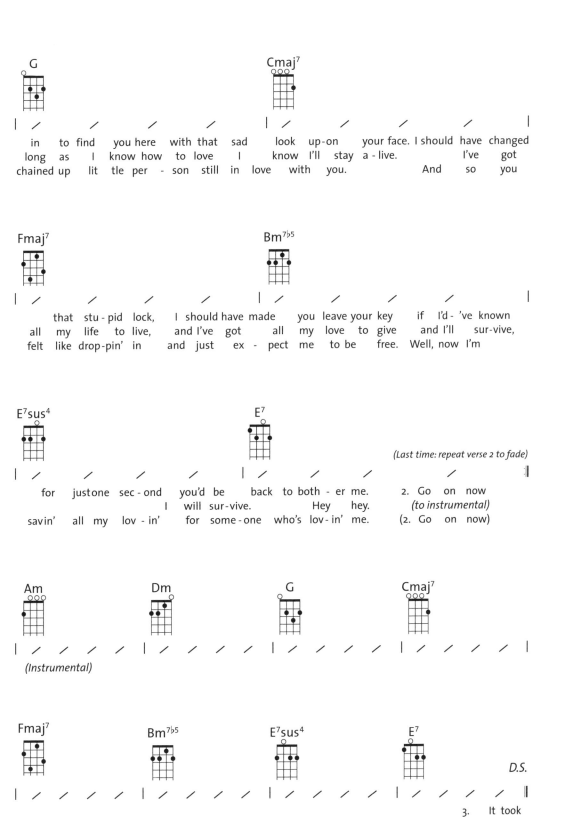

is you is or is you ain't my baby?

Words & Music by Billy Austin & Louis Jorda

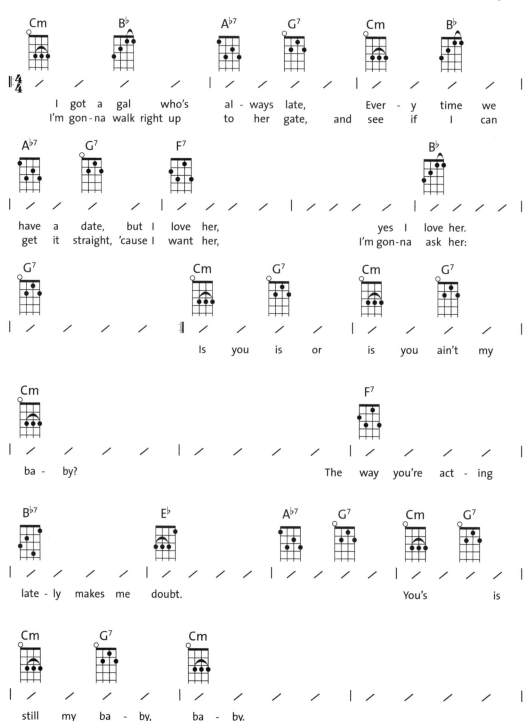

F⁷   B♭⁷   E♭   E♭⁷

/ / / / | / / / / | / / / / | / / / / |

Seems my flame in   your   heart done gone   out.   A

A♭   A♭m⁷   E♭

/ / / / | / / / / | / / / / |

wo - man   is   a   crea - ture   that   has   al - ways   been

E♭⁷   A♭   D♭⁷

/ / / / | / / / / | / / / / |

strange.   Just   when you're   sure   of   one   you   find   she's

C⁷   Fm   G⁷   Cm   G⁷

/ / / / | / / / / | / / / / |

gone   and   made   a   change.   Is   you   is   or

Cm   G⁷   Cm

/ / / / | / / / / | / / / / |

is   you   ain't   my   ba - by?

F⁷   B♭⁷   D♭⁷   C⁷

/ / / / | / / / / | / / / / | / / / / |

May - be ba - by's   found some - bo - dy   new,   or

F⁷   B♭⁷   E♭

/ / / / | / / / / | / / / / ‖

is   my   ba - by   still   my   ba - by   true.

33

run

Words & Music by Gary Lightbody, Jonathan Quinn,
Mark McClelland, Nathan Connolly & Iain Archer

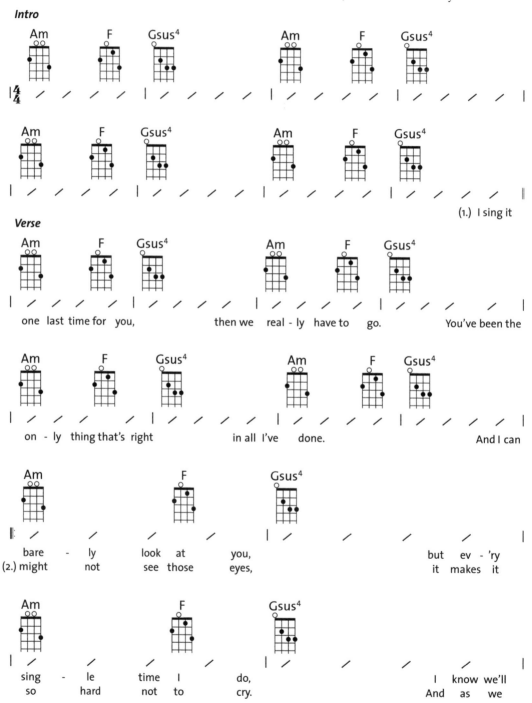

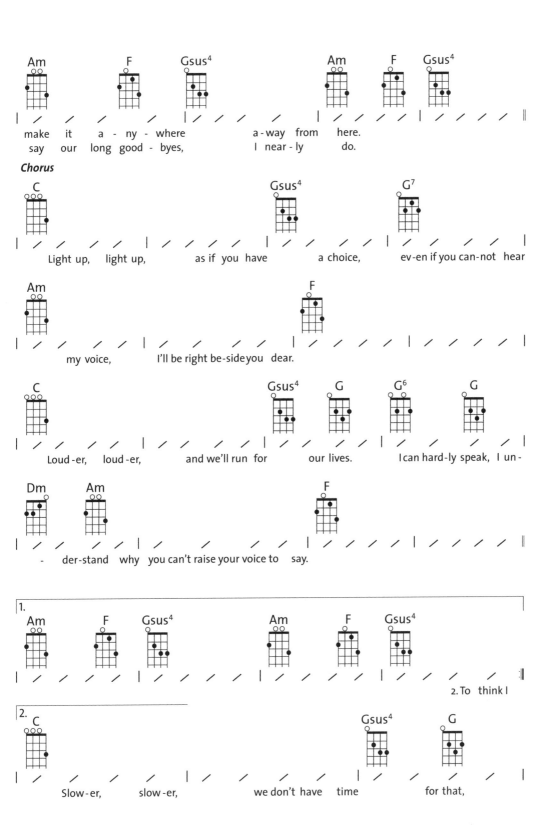

Am   **F**   **Gsus⁴**   **Am**   **F**   **Gsus⁴**

make it a - ny - where   a - way from here.
say our long good - byes,   I near - ly do.

Chorus

C   **Gsus⁴**   **G⁷**

Light up, light up,   as if you have   a choice,   ev-en if you can-not hear

Am   **F**

my voice,   I'll be right be-side you dear.

C   **Gsus⁴**   **G**   **G⁶**   **G**

Loud - er, loud - er,   and we'll run for   our lives.   I can hard-ly speak, I un-

Dm   **Am**   **F**

- der-stand why you can't raise your voice to say.

1.

Am   **F**   **Gsus⁴**   **Am**   **F**   **Gsus⁴**

2. To think I

2.

C   **Gsus⁴**   **G**

Slow - er, slow - er,   we don't have time   for that,

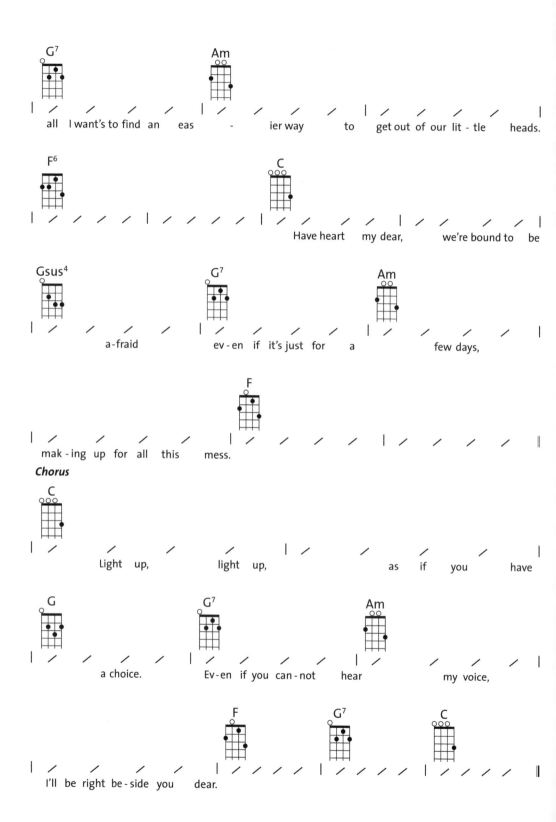

G⁷   Am

| / | / | / | / | | / | / | / | | / | / | / | / |

all I want's to find an eas -   ier way   to   get out of our lit - tle   heads.

F⁶   C

Have heart my dear,   we're bound to be

Gsus⁴   G⁷   Am

a-fraid   ev - en if it's just for a   few days,

F

mak - ing up for all this mess.

Chorus

C

Light up,   light up,   as if you   have

G   G⁷   Am

a choice.   Ev-en if you can-not hear   my voice,

F   G⁷   C

I'll be right be - side you dear.

36

should i stay or should i go

Words & Music by Joe Strummer & Mick Jones

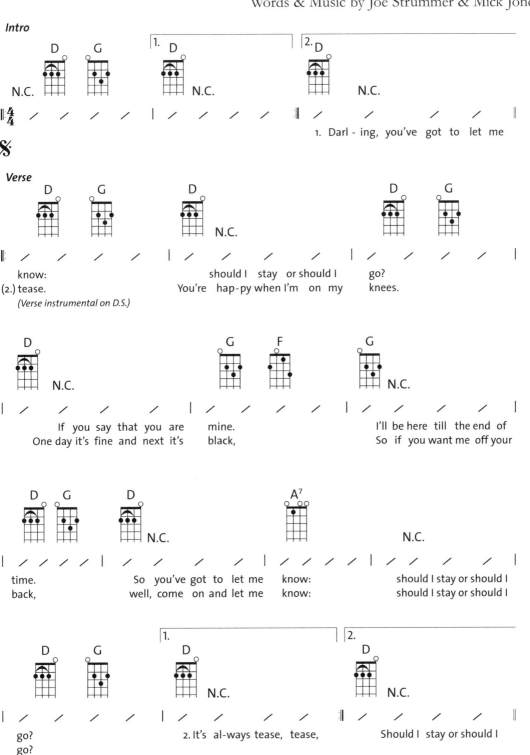

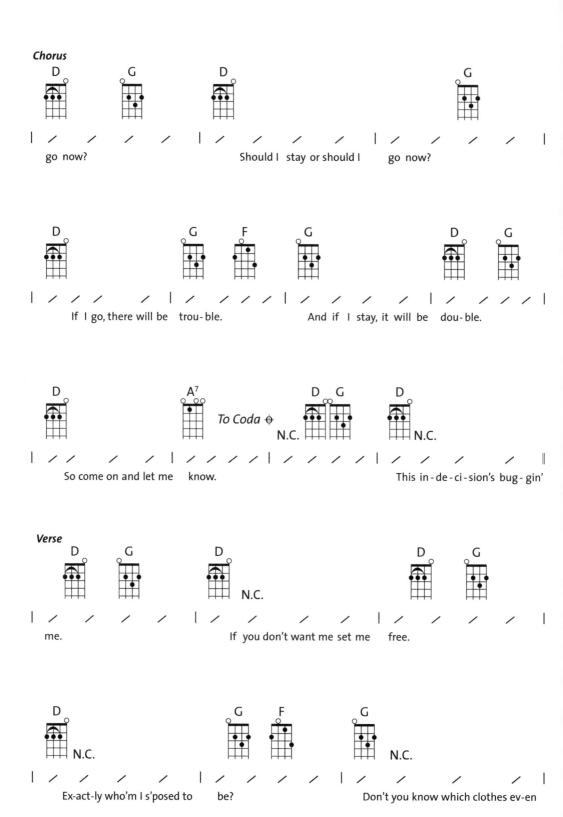

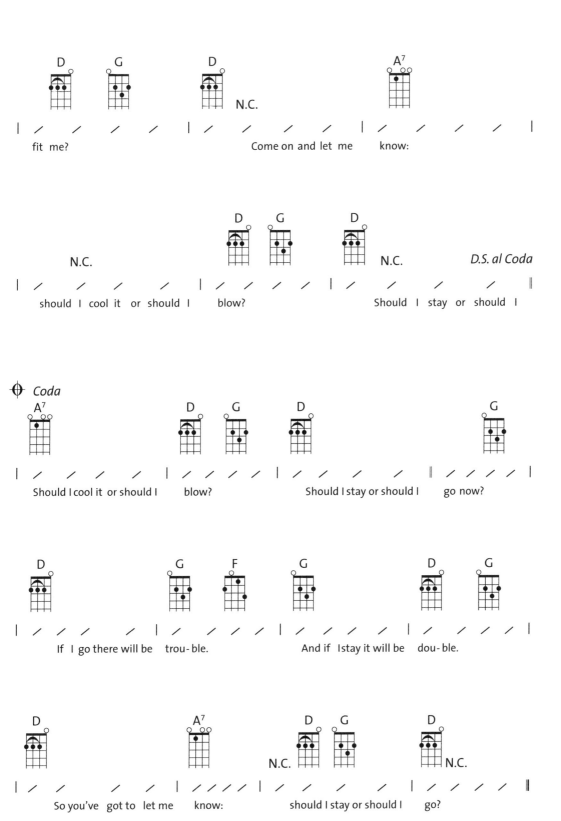

wonderwall

Words & Music by Noel Gallagher

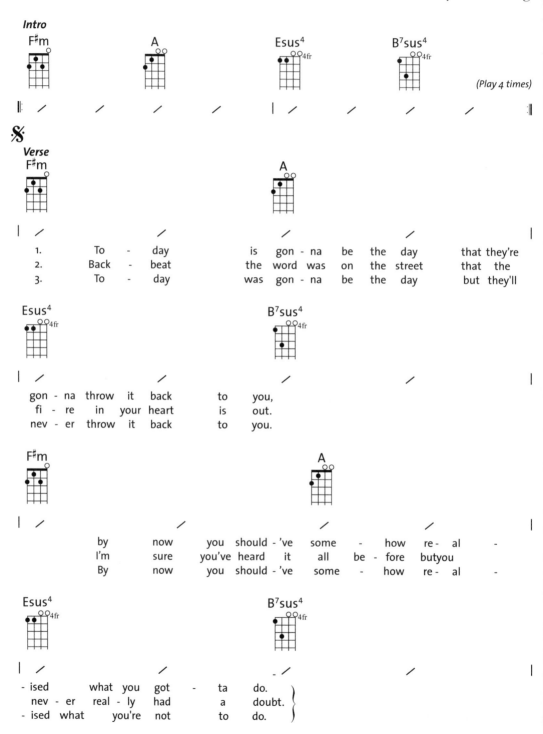

F#m　　　　　　　　　　　　**A**

| ╱ 　　　　　　 ╱ 　　　　　　 ╱ 　　　　　　 ╱ 　　　　 |

I　don't　be - lieve　　　that　an　-　y - bo　-　dy

Esus⁴　　　　　　　　　　　**B⁷sus⁴**

| ╱ 　　　　　　 ╱ 　　　　　　 ╱ 　　　　　　 ╱ 　　　　 |

feels　　　　the　way　I　　　do　　　　a - bout　　you　now.

1.
Dsus²　　　　**Esus⁴**　　　　**B⁷sus⁴**

| ╱ 　 ╱ 　 ╱ 　 ╱ 　| ╱ 　 ╱ 　 ╱ 　 ╱ 　 ╱ ‖

2, 3.
F#m　　　　**A**　　　　　**Esus⁴**　　　　**B⁷sus⁴**

| ╱ 　 ╱ 　 ╱ 　 ╱ 　| ╱ 　 ╱ 　 ╱ 　 ╱ 　|

And all

D　　　　　　　**E**　　　　　　　　　　**F#m**

| ╱ 　 ╱ 　 ╱ 　 ╱ 　| ╱ 　 ╱ 　 ╱ 　 ╱ 　|

the　roads　we　have　to　walk　　are　wind　-　ing　　and all
the　roads　that　lead　you　there　were　wind　-　ing　　and all

D　　　　　　　**E**　　　　　　　　　　**F#m**

| ╱ 　 ╱ 　 ╱ 　 ╱ 　| ╱ 　 ╱ 　 ╱ 　 ╱ 　|

the　lights　that　lead　us　there　are　blind　-　ing.
the　lights　that　light　the way　are　blind　-　ing.

41

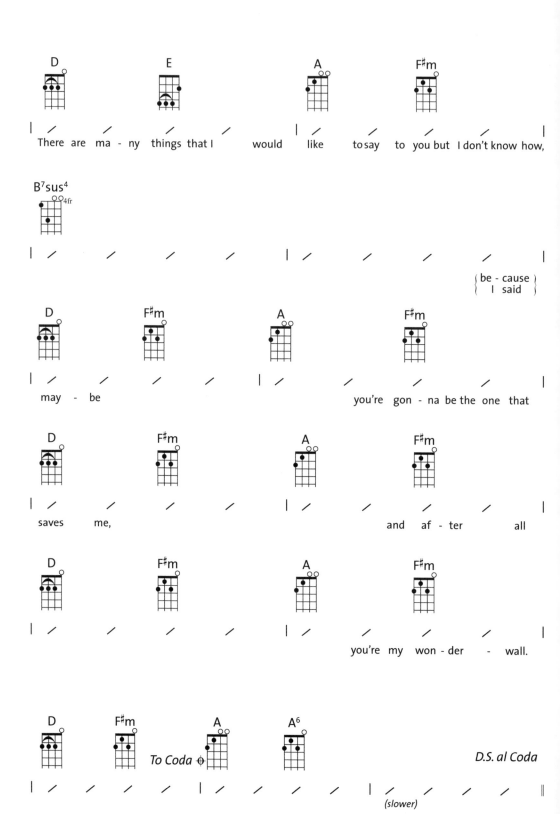

D   E   A   F#m

There are ma - ny things that I   would   like   to say   to you but I don't know how,

B⁷sus⁴

{ be - cause }
{ I said }

D   F#m   A   F#m

may - be   you're gon - na be the one that

D   F#m   A   F#m

saves   me,   and af - ter   all

D   F#m   A   F#m

you're my won - der - wall.

D   F#m   A   A⁶

To Coda ⊕   *D.S. al Coda*

(slower)

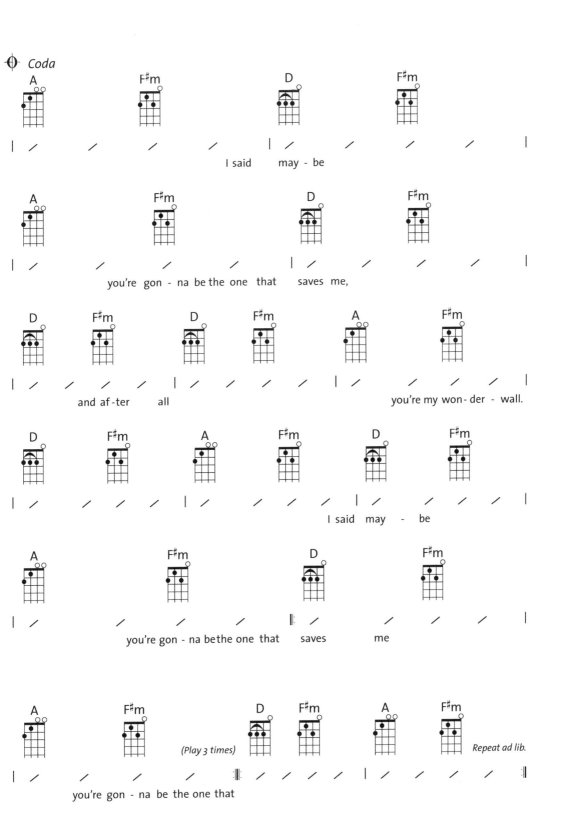

Coda

I said   may - be

you're gon - na be the one that   saves me,

and af - ter   all   you're my won - der - wall.

I said may - be

you're gon - na be the one that   saves   me

(Play 3 times)   Repeat ad lib.

you're gon - na be the one that

43

viva la vida

Words & Music by Guy Berryman, Chris Martin, Jon Buckland & Will Champion

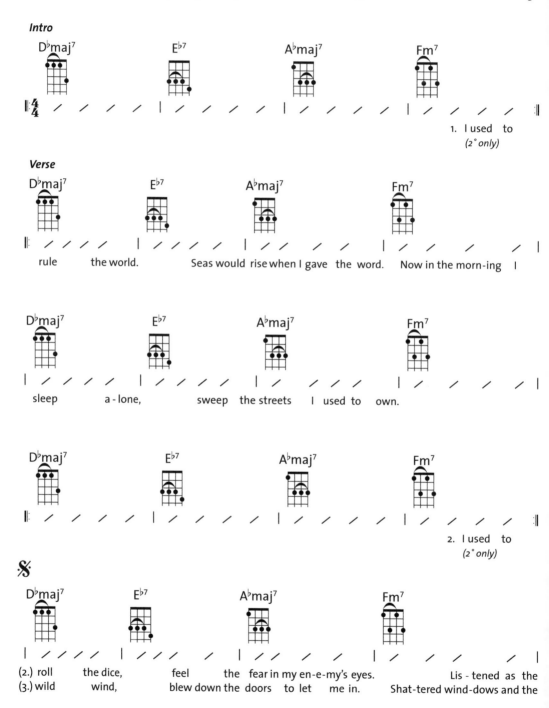

D♭maj7 · **E♭7** · **A♭maj7** · **Fm7**

crowd would sing, "Now the old king is dead, long live the king." One min-ute I
sound of drums. Peo - ple could-n't be-lieve what I'd be-come. Rev - o - lu-tion-

D♭maj7 · **E♭7** · **A♭maj7** · **Fm7**

held the key, next the walls were closed on me and I dis-cov-ered that my
- ar - ies wait for my head on a sil - ver plate. Just a pup-pet on a

D♭maj7 · **E♭7** · **A♭maj7** · **Fm7**

cas - tles stand up-on pil - lars of salt and pil-lars of sand.
lone - ly string. Oh, who would ev-er wan-na be king?

𝄋 𝄋

Chorus

D♭maj7 · **E♭7** · **A♭maj7** · **Fm7**

hear Je - ru-sa-lem bells a-ring-ing. Ro - man Cav-al-ry choirs are sing-ing.

D♭maj7 · **E♭7** · **A♭maj7** · **Fm7**

Be my mir-ror, my sword, and shield. My mis-sion-ar - ies in a for - eign field.

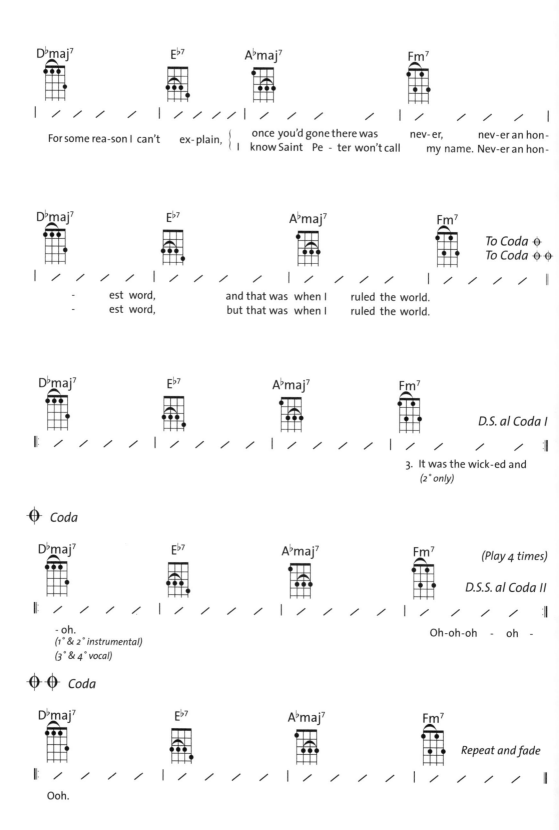

D♭maj⁷   E♭⁷   A♭maj⁷   Fm⁷

For some rea-son I can't   ex-plain, { once you'd gone there was   nev-er,   nev-er an hon-
                         { I   know Saint Pe - ter won't call   my name. Nev-er an hon-

D♭maj⁷   E♭⁷   A♭maj⁷   Fm⁷

To Coda ⊕
To Coda ⊕ ⊕

-   est word,   and that was when I   ruled the world.
-   est word,   but that was when I   ruled the world.

D♭maj⁷   E♭⁷   A♭maj⁷   Fm⁷

D.S. al Coda I

3. It was the wick-ed and
(2° only)

⊕ *Coda*

D♭maj⁷   E♭⁷   A♭maj⁷   Fm⁷

(Play 4 times)

D.S.S. al Coda II

- oh.
(1° & 2° instrumental)
(3° & 4° vocal)

                                Oh-oh-oh - oh -

⊕ ⊕ *Coda*

D♭maj⁷   E♭⁷   A♭maj⁷   Fm⁷

Repeat and fade

Ooh.

you raise me up

Words & Music by Rolf Løvland & Brendan Graham

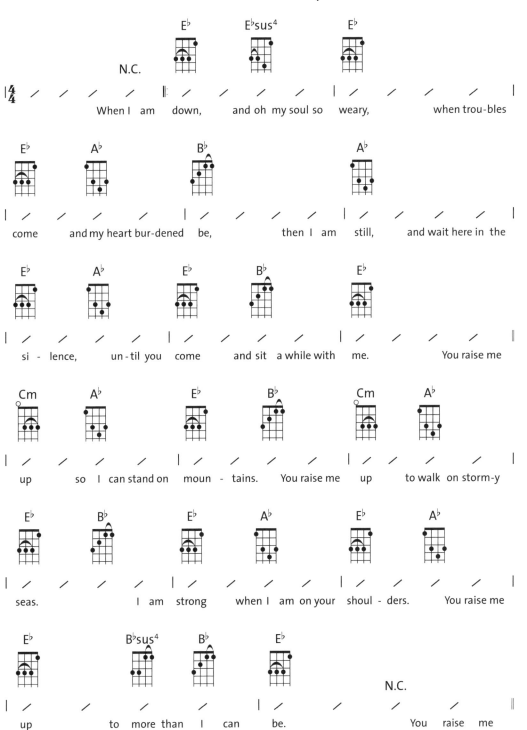

2 3 4 5 6 7 8
12/09(17254